The
BEACH to HELL

Omaha Beach

6th june 1944

Patrick Bousquet-Schneeweis & Michel Giard

The
BEACH to HELL

Omaha Beach

6th june 1944

OREP
EDITIONS

To our friend Gilles Perrault,
who has followed us, supported us and
encouraged us for many years...
The authors.

To Cécile and Jacques Glacet
who took care of me
during my darkest years.
P.B-S.

Patrick Bousquet-Schneeweis is an author of tales, poetry and novels for children and adults, many of which have been rewarded with literary prizes, and also of lyrics. He shares his time between the towns of Hendaye and Paris. He has developed a passion for the history of the two world wars and... for cats. He has also produced comic strips with his friend and colleague Régis Hector, with whom he published *Les aventures d'Oscar et Mauricette*.

Michel Giard is an eclectic writer who has published around fifty works, essentially focusing on Normandy and on maritime history. He is a historian, lecturer, traveller, chronicler for the France Bleu Cotentin radio station and has already published, with Orep, *Phares et feux de Normandie* and *Les Chansons normandes*.

Foreword

Although based on accurate documentation, this book is a work of fiction.

The authors.

The hospital ship

It was the evening of the 6th of June 1944 and the USS *Samuel Chase* split through the cold grey waters of the English Channel towards England.

This troop transport vessel had hastily been transformed into a hospital ship due to the heavy losses suffered by the Americans during the early hours of the D-Day Landings.

On board, hundreds of crammed troops, from simple soldiers to high-ranking officers, who, a few hours previously, had tried to set foot on Omaha Beach under deadly German gunfire.

William Bishop was among these poor souls, attended to by sympathetic carers – often somewhat overwhelmed by the immensity of their task.

Bishop, a GI[1] among thousands, had come from his faraway homeland of America to combat Nazism and to offer the world newfound freedom...

---

1. This abbreviation signifies a US Army infantryman.

William Bishop gradually regained consciousness amidst the groans, cries of suffering, machines, sailors and nurses as they rushed to and fro, not forgetting the raging waves as they thrust against the steel hull of the ship.

Still wearing the top of his battledress, he lays on a blood-splattered stretcher on the deck of the USS *Samuel Chase*, along with dozens of other brothers in arms.

As he struggled to turn his head, he could not help but shudder when he noticed a young military chaplain with a tiny wooden cross in his hand, busy giving the last rites to a young infantryman, barely older than William himself.

A little further away, an officer ordered someone to urgently go and fetch doses of morphine to relieve the pain of a soldier who suffered serious burns to the face.

Bishop rapidly passed his hand over his face to wipe off the sweat that was running down his forehead.

He discovered his hand covered with a sticky substance that was difficult to define – a mixture of dirt, blood, dust and petrol.

Visibly relieved to discover that his face was intact, he tried to sit upright, but was almost immediately seized by an intense pain in his right leg.

"Don't move, young man; listen to me, be reasonable!" a stretcher-bearer, whose eyes were hollowed out with exhaustion, advised as he leaned over him.

Bishop obeyed as he cautiously patted the bandage that was pressing into the top of his thigh.

At that very instant, he recalled how he had paddled his way through less than 20 inches of water surrounded by bodies and obstacles of all sorts, as an enemy machine gun took him, along with his buddies, as its target, on what was the first wave of assault on *Easy Red*, one of the *Omaha Beach* landing zones.

The smiling face of his English fiancée, Jenny, suddenly appeared to him. At the same time, a desperate ear-splitting scream resounded from the lower deck...

A little later, a sailor asked a nurse, as he nodded to Bishop, "Do you think we'll be able to save his leg?"

"No idea mate. There's always a risk of gangrene. It all depends on how long it takes us to reach..."

The end of the sentence was lost in the thunderous clamour of a squadron of Typhoons[2] on their way back from a low-altitude bombing mission.

---

2. British fighter-bomber. Thanks to its rockets, it was to become a formidable tank "killer".

Panic-stricken at the idea of dying aboard this hospital ship without leaving the slightest trace, the tiniest testimony of his dramatic adventure, William Bishop took his ever-loyal small leather notebook out of his pocket.

A few minutes later, lulled by the words of a song sung by an unknown shipmate, Bishop closed his eyes – a long moment – so as to concentrate as hard as he could. Then, nervously, he jotted on the first page of his notebook, using a tiny pencil...

My name is William Bishop.

I am 22 years old and I come from a small village in the state of Virginia, located around twenty miles from Richmond and where, in another life, I used to be a motor mechanic.

I belong to the US 1st Infantry Division, the famous Big Red One.

The division that had been entrusted with the mission to land on Omaha Beach, in the Easy Red sector, on the 6th of June 1944.

It had all started three months earlier...

In England

25th February 1944.

I can't believe my eyes.
The south of England, where my division is based,
is now reminiscent of a huge car park built by an
architect who seems to have lost his compass.
All around, Jeeps[3], ambulances, trucks, guns, tanks
and planes are lined up, one behind another, just
like in a parade, along roads and in fields, waiting
to take part in one of the greatest military operations
of all time: the Normandy Landings.
And that's not counting the soldiers, infantrymen,
paratroopers, airmen, sailors, commandos and
bomb disposal experts that have invaded up to the
tiniest little village along the coast, under the
sometimes surprised, admiring or rather
compassionate gaze of the entire local population.
At our level, nobody knows what day or what time
this landing's going to happen...
Some, like my buddy Peter Johnson, say it'll be in
Pas-de-Calais. Others, like one of the paras from the
101st Airborne I was talking to this very morning,

---

3. Refer to glossary.

are betting on Normandy, or even Brittany which is home to many ports and harbours.

As for the exact date.... nobody knows, for that will greatly depend on the weather. To be quite honest, I wouldn't like to be in the shoes of the guy who's gonna give the order to launch this incredible and fantastic war machine to attack "Fortress Europe". I'm talking about our big chief Eisenhower! What a responsibility he carries!

As for those on the other side, the "Jerries", the "Krauts" or the "Schleus[4]", as we call them here, all we know is that they're brave, often fanatical, and that they're ready and waiting for us.

Under the impetus of the former Afrika Korps commander, Field Marshal Rommel, they have built an impressive and impregnable concrete wall, interspersed with bunkers, guns and machine guns; they call it the "Atlantic Wall[5]".

According to the latest word that's going round – be it truth or rumour – millions of mines have been placed on the beaches and along the coast, not forgetting the various obstacles scattered along the shoreline to sink our landing barges and to thwart our inland progression. In a nutshell, we all know that this landing is going to be no pleasure cruise, even if we also know for sure that, when the day comes, we'll have staunch support from the paras, the air force and the navy.

---

4. Derogatory terms used to describe the German soldiers.

5. Refer to glossary.

Along with two other mates, Peter Johnson, who I've already told you about, and James Mercury, a strapping lad born and bred in Springfield, we're lucky to have been accommodated by locals, which is not the case for all of the guys from our section.

Mr and Mrs Bellamy, a retired couple whose son, Frederick, was a Spitfire[6] pilot and was killed during the Battle of Britain[7], are bending over backwards to make sure our stay is as pleasant as possible in their gorgeous little village called Sand Creek.

We sleep, all three of us, on the second floor of a pretty and typically English house overlooking a floral garden which Mrs Bellamy looks after with much enthusiasm. Much to my delight, our hosts have a big dog, a rather crazy but extremely affectionate mongrel called Sam. He sometimes reminds me of Blacky, my old Labrador, the one I left inconsolable on the other side of the Atlantic, the morning I enlisted.

Sand Creek has, by force of circumstance, become our new home. The days we spend here are relatively repetitive and they can also prove desperately long.

For, indeed, we share our time between chores, intensive training, mock combat, weapon cleaning and maintenance, parades in front of impassive officers and interminable marches with a 45 to 65 pound kit bag, come rain, hail or shine.

---

6. British fighter plane that proved particularly effective during the Battle of Britain.

7. Refer to glossary.

Boredom, fatigue and tension can contribute to some hot moods, rivalry and even fighting between the different soldiers and corps that collectively comprise the largest armada of all time.

Even if these skirmishes are few and far between, let's not forget who our real enemy is!

These fights are often violent, due to someone cheating at a game of cards, an unpleasant look, an ironic smile, an insignificant jibe, on an evening's leave, for one glass too many with the girl in the corner who's refused or, on the contrary, has accepted a dance with one of us.

This short digression suddenly brings to mind the one who now holds a very special place in my heart and in my life: Jennifer.

My darling Jenny. Twenty years-old, blond with turquoise blue eyes, a history of art student, pretty, elegant and thoughtful at the same time.

Jennifer, an oasis of tenderness in an immensity of violence.

Jenny

"Hey Bishop!" a red-faced soldier cried at that very instant after having struggled to decipher my name on my torn battledress, which was spattered with mud and blood. "What are you up to? Don't tell me that, in your state, you still have the courage to write poems or to do a philosophy lesson?"

"Not really mate! I'm just jotting down a few impressions, a few..."

I didn't have time to finish my sentence.

The man stared at me attentively then, when he discovered my division, on the top of my left shoulder, he suddenly asked,

"You belong to the 1st Infantry Division? The illustrious *Big Red One?*"

"Indeed."

"You were on Omaha then? I heard it was really tough there."

"Pretty tough yeah. I landed with the first wave of assault in the *Easy Red* sector. I lost a good few of my buddies there. Apparently, it was the same on *Dog* and *Fox*! I'm sorry, but I don't particularly want to talk about it. It was so horrible..."

"OK. I understand. I won't insist."

"What about you?"

"I'm Douglas Hillman. I belonged to the 82nd Airborne. On the night of the 5th to the 6th of June, we were the target of several German coastal batteries; our *Dakota*[8] dropped us further than planned and, tonnes of guys from my stick[9] were gunned down by the "Schleus" or drowned in the marshes, bogged down by their heavy kit bags. I was luckier, well I suppose so," he added as he lifted his right arm which was shrouded in a huge bandage.

"What happened to you?"

"Grenade fragments during an encounter with an enemy patrol!" Hillman explained with a strange smile. "But I managed to escape after shooting up an officer. I still don't know if they'll be able to save my hand. Anyway, this goddamn war is over for me... That's good news at least, isn't it?"

"Hey Douglas, come and see!" yelled a voice with a hint of a Midwest accent. "Fancy a quick game of poker? With just one hand, you'll have trouble cheating this time!"

"I'm on my way guys!"

---

8. The Douglas C-47 or Dakota was a plane used to drop American paratroopers on the night of the 5th to the 6th of June 1944.

9. Stick: a group of paratroopers jumping from the same plane.

As soon as Douglas Hillman had left, Bishop set to continuing his account. Where was I? Oh yes, Jenny. My dear and sweet Jenny.

It happened on the 6th of last May. A date I'll never forget.

I was on my way home from the King's Arms, the local pub on the outskirts of town. I'd swallowed down a few beers along with James, Peter and a good few other guys from the 29th Infantry Division. At around 10 pm, I could feel I was in for a terrible headache and I'd decided to go home to bed, leaving my two chums at their card game and their darts tournament.

At the entrance to the village, I was overtaken by a vehicle with its lights out, zigzagging at breakneck speed along the track.

A little later, I was around 50 yards from the Bellamy's house when I heard furious barking from the hedgerow that ran alongside the road. Cautiously, I drew closer and discovered a young blond-haired girl around 20 years old, lying on the ground next to a bicycle with a twisted handlebar and watched over by a dog I recognized to be my friendly companion Sam.

"What happened Miss?" I asked as I warded off the dog's affectionate onslaught.

"I've just been knocked down by a Jeep driven by an absolute madman! This dog must have heard me

screaming, because he came almost immediately. He looks like he already knows you!"

I simply nodded as I asked her if she had been hurt. "No, thankfully. It was more frightening than anything else!" she replied as she stood up and dusted her dress. "But my poor bike will never recover..."

A few seconds later, as she held out her hand to me, she added,

"By the way, my name is Jennifer Aston. Jenny to my friends. I live in Sparrowbridge, a small village on the edge of the forest, around 3 miles from here. Are you American?" she pursued, glancing at my uniform.

"I..."

"That's good news," she interrupted, "I love America!"

I think that it was at the very instant when she uttered those words that I fell in love with Jenny...

Since then, Jenny and I have been inseparable.

For us, Sand Creek has become a haven of peace, love and shared complicity.

We experienced the most marvellous, tender and intense of moments there. All the more intense for everything here, every minute of every day, reminded us of the fragility of life, the lost flight of happiness and the imminent danger that lay in wait.

Less than a month later, with the rest of my division, I boarded the troop transport ship that was to take us to Normandy; never, for a single second, did I imagine the horror that awaited us...

The wait

4th June 1944.

I was finishing a hard-fought game of cards with Peter, when James suddenly dashed into our room and, almost at the top of his voice, yelled,
"William, Peter, it's for tomorrow!"
"Hey, calm down!" replied Peter fuming as he laid down four kings. "Do you often take to screaming like that? Because of you, I've lost my concentration and William, as usual, is going to take advantage and strip me of a good few dollars! So, what's for tomorrow then?"
"D-Day[10] guys!" James excitedly continued, "I was told earlier by a French guy from the Kieffer[11] commando. All we need now is Ike's[12] go-ahead! Do you realise, we're off, we're off! After all those months waiting! We're finally gonna show those bastardly "Krauts" what we can do! Adolf, that moustached little swine, had better watch out!"

---

10. "Decision-Day".

11. Refer to glossary.

12. The nickname given to General Eisenhower, Commander in Chief of the Allied forces.

I couldn't quite explain why, but I had trouble believing it.

It was as if I was convinced that some last-minute event would occur and would force the Allied high command to postpone the Landings we'd all been hoping for, for such a long time.

And, as my two buddies began a merry scalp dance around the room, I headed for the bottom of the garden to seek refuge and to conceal my doubts and, above all, my sadness.

Indeed, if what James had just told us was true, that meant that Jennifer and I would soon be separated. Perhaps forever... An absolute catastrophe for both of us!

You get used to happiness so quickly...

And I was right.

A few hours later, as we were just about to board, we were told that, due to appalling weather conditions, operation "Overlord[13]" had been postponed by Eisenhower.

You can imagine the frame of mind we were in when he learned of that darned delay!

We were preparing to return to our barracks under lashing rain, when a superior officer from the 116th Infantry Regiment I belonged to told us of our future destination, perhaps in the hope that it would cheer us up: Colleville-sur-Mer, a small Norman village

---

13. Name given by the Allies to the Normandy Landings.

on the shores of a beach that had been codenamed Omaha...
Strangely, this information was of no particular consequence to me.

The big day

5th June 1944.

This time, it was the big day!
General Eisenhower had finally given the order we
were all waiting for.
He had very probably done so reluctantly for the
weather had barely improved since the previous day.
But what did it matter since, in a few hours, we
would finally reach France! France, of which - I
must admit and much to my regret - I know nothing
or so little, apart from the fact that they drink wine
there and that the girls are pretty.

*

On the dawn of this particular 6th of June, the
view that unravelled before me from the troop
transport vessel I had boarded was grandiose,
incredible, almost unreal.
Imagine 6,000 boats, from battleships to tank
transport vessels, from cruisers to submarine chasers,
from destroyers to minesweepers, from landing
barges to hospital ships, all of them supported by

around 11,000 planes, bombers, fighters and gliders! Suddenly, despite the fear that had begun to twist my guts, I felt slightly more reassured or, if you prefer, a little less anxious...

I could already imagine, with somewhat unhealthy delight, how the first German soldiers would feel when they discovered, through their binoculars, this formidable armada emerging from the sea haze...

*

It was cloudy and the sea was still as choppy.

The guns aboard our ships were already incessantly pounding the coast in front of us.

A genuine deluge of iron and fire was raining down on the enemy positions which, strangely to me, did not retaliate.

Or at least not yet...

Just like hundreds of other infantrymen, our faces beaten by the sea spray, I carefully climbed down the nets that were fixed to the troop transport vessels towards the landing barges.

It proved to be a dangerous manoeuvre, fatal even for some, due to the terrible wind that was now arriving in huge gusts and hollowing out the sea swell.

Aboard my LCVP[14], the men were deep in concentration, tense, silent. Many of them suffered from appalling seasickness.

"Poor guy! I feel so sorry for him," a GI, chilled to the bone, said to me as he nodded to my friend James, who had put down his rifle to vomit more conveniently inside his helmet.

"Hang on in there mate, you ain't seen nothing yet!" a sergeant amusedly replied as he gave him a friendly tap on the shoulder.

A little later, I noticed Peter Johnson with a rosary in his hands as he murmured a prayer.

I waved in his direction to wish him good luck for later. But did he see me?

What were we waiting for? I couldn't fathom it out. The LCVPs had been turning round in circles for several minutes, none of them deciding to head for the foreshore.

To kill time, I checked my Garand semi-automatic rifle charger once more, then, a few seconds later, I took a photograph out of the pocket of my battledress, a photograph I kept with me at all times. It was a picture of Jenny, in my friend Sam's arms, as they danced a rather crazy waltz. I had taken it during my last leave on a small deserted beach.

A few days before our separation, after kissing me, Jenny made me promise I'd keep it with me on the day of the assault.

---

14. Refer to glossary.

As the gunfire from the ships gradually increased in range, I suddenly felt the shudder of the LCVP engine.

"We're off guys!" a lieutenant yelled as he brandished his bayonet. "Good luck to you all! And don't forget to keep your heads down and look after your guns!"

"Yeah, they could well come in handy later on!" a beaming GI ironically replied as he turned to look at me.

I didn't answer. I didn't particularly feel like joking. Despite our orders, I carefully looked overboard for a few seconds.

Far away in the distance, amidst the roar of the explosions and the plumes of smoke, the German artillery batteries remained silent.

Was this a good sign? Or a bad sign? We would find out in no time...

They're coming!

In the low glow of his lighter, Panzergrenadier Hans Kuerten scrutinised the face of his watch. It was five o'clock in the morning on the 6th of June 1944 and Hans couldn't help but shudder as he affectionately ran his hand over the muzzle of his MG 42 machine gun.

The Allied aviation had been flying overhead relentlessly throughout the night and he could perceive the distant flames of the bombed towns and villages further inland.

The temperature had lowered over the last few minutes. Thankfully, his guard duty would be over in less than three hours.

Kuerten found consolation in the thought of the hot coffee he would soon be taking in the bunker commanded by Oberleutnant Klaus Dietrich and located around 50 yards from WN[15] 68, where he was currently standing along with several other soldiers, all of them far older than himself.

---

15. Abbreviation of *Widerstandnest*, a German word signifying resistance nest.

Kuerten had just celebrated his twenty-fifth birthday and was, in times of peace, a civilian bakery worker. He belonged to the 352nd Infantry Division in charge of defending the Colleville-sur-Mer sector.

From his strongpoint, in the early hours of dusk, immediately in front of his machine gun, he could see the beach below, covered with obstacles in the form of Czech hedgehogs, Belgian gates, Rommel's "asparagus[16]", not forgetting the barbed wire, "chevaux de frise" and mines – intended to easily drive back any assailant. Or at least that's what Field Marshal Rommel had stated during his last inspection, a fortnight earlier.

But when would the enemy come? Hans had no idea. Certainly not today, he thought to himself, the weather was far too bad.

Joachim Rudel was sitting right next to him on a case of ammunition; he was the chief gunner for the MG 42 and was an extremely friendly chap who had fought in Stalingrad. He was busy writing a letter to Ingrid, his fiancée.

"Rather cold, no?" Kuerten noted as he discreetly lit up a cigarette.

"You're quite right Hans, but believe me, it was far worse on the Russian Front!"

---

16. Refer to glossary.

"I'd still be glad to go indoors for a few minutes to warm up," replied Rudel as he took a handkerchief out of his uniform pocket. "In any case, there's very little chance of them landing in such weather!"

"You never know," mumbled Ludwig Penel, the young machine gun artilleryman. "We've already seen some pretty crazy things. Just think about Hannibal who crossed the Alps with his elephants... The Romans would never have believed that was possible either!"

"Stop it Ludwig! You're going to bring us bad luck!"

Penel shrugged his shoulders as he scrutinised the horizon with his binoculars.

He was about to place them back on his chest when he noticed what looked like threatening shadows on their way to the coast.

Then, in just a few seconds, as if a gigantic knife had slashed through it, the curtain of mist was torn open, giving way to the silhouettes of hundreds of vessels that collectively formed a continuous wall.

"Dear God, protect us!" Penel whispered before he anxiously cried to his colleagues, who were still oblivious to the scene,

"Hans, Joachim, they're coming! They dared, despite this darned weather! They're coming! There they are, right in front of us! Quick, we need to warn the others!"

"What are you on about Ludwig? You've gone mad!"

"Are you blind or what?" Penel furiously resumed as he pointed out to the high seas. "The Landings, the blasted Landings you didn't want to believe in, well, they're today, they're now and they're for us!"

The assault

Lined up as if for a parade, the barges were now heading for the shoreline.

In our sodden uniforms, soaked by the huge waves that surged inside our LCVP, our wills were weak and the tension was almost tangible.

Suddenly, when we were still at least 600 yards from the beach, the first shell from a coastal battery landed to the left of us. It was followed by another, on our right this time, fired from a villa that had been transformed into a bunker... then a third one. Our entire fleet was soon surrounded by increasingly intense enemy fire.

Increasingly accurate.

Increasingly deadly.

"I thought our boats and our planes had done their job and reduced those bastardly "Schleus" to silence!" a GI behind me enquired as he nervously crossed his fingers.

"They had to leave us some work to do!" another one joked in a half-hearted tone. "It was the same when I landed in Sicily!"

An LCVP just behind us was hit head-on. We saw a few survivors trying to escape from the blazing barge only to drown almost instantaneously under the weight of their packs.

In the meantime, hell was raging...

Our LCVP endeavoured as best it could to avoid, not only the enemy projectiles, but also the other Allied vessels that were thrown off course, not forgetting the wrecked barges and the many soldiers who, after going overboard, were doing their best to swim through total chaos.

All around us, all we could hear was howls of suffering, calls for help and explosions.

"Watch out! You're taking us straight to the mines!" a corporal yelled to the pilot of our barge.

The latter gave a brisk blow to the rudder and dodged the obstacle just in time.

That was when I saw my first dead body.

A guy barely older than me, his childlike face floating, drifting, his right arm torn off. Nearby, a GI wounded in the head was floating on his back and begging for someone to come and help him.

"Nobody stops! Don't look after the wounded!" an officer shouted in a toneless voice. "That's an order!"

We were at least thirty yards from the beach when we received orders to leave the LCVP.

In a huge scramble, I leapt into the water in the middle of all my buddies, seeking refuge behind the steel tetrahedrons that surfaced here and there between the foam of the waves.

On several occasions, as I was jostled by the treacherous waves, I was nearly dragged underwater by the weight of my kit bag. At the same time a machine gun had chosen me as its target; however, I managed to resurface and to continue my landward progression under the raging whistle of the enemy bullets.

A GI, hit straight in the face, twirled round in front of me, then sank immediately. Another one, who was trying to get rid of his broken radio was almost cut in two by a piece of shrapnel.

By now, I was paddling in water that was already reddened with the blood of the poor victims whose lifeless bodies drifted alongside the dead fish, equipment and abandoned weapons.

The shell of a Sherman tank that had struck a mine was ablaze next to a "Belgian gate", emitting a cloud of thick, black smoke. As I was struggling to escape the bullets from the machine gun that had, once more, chosen me as its target, wreaking total carnage in our ranks, I heard someone behind me screaming my name,

"William ! William!"

I cautiously turned round. It was my friend James, as he helped out an infantryman who was tangled up in his kit, who was asking me to join him behind the blazing tank.

James. My old friend James. An extraordinarily kind and generous chap.

That was the last time I saw him alive.

Behind his MG 42, placed directly on the ground, pointed towards the fleet of embarkations that had just unloaded their cargo of soldiers almost immediately opposite WN 68, Hans Kuerten patiently awaited the right time to fire.

Within sight, he now had dozens of soldiers who were struggling counter current in the hope of reaching the shore a little faster.

Kuerten was incapable of deciding on a target. There were too many of them. Why that man rather than the other one?

"Open fire!" the chief gunner suddenly ordered with an exaggerated smile.

Kuerten's finger slowly pressed the trigger of his MG 42.

The weapon shuddered against his shoulder as the first stick of projectiles skimmed across the surface of the water without hitting a single target.

"Hans, lift your backsight adjuster!" Ludwig Penel advised him as he took a new belt from the ammunition box.

The second spray of bullets was more accurate and sent ten men flying to the ground on the sandy beach.

Penel couldn't help but applaud like a child to congratulate him.

Kuerten then aimed at a tank that was already ablaze and towards which a lone soldier was trying to head.

His third burst hit a GI who was helping another one near a burning armoured vehicle. "You got that bastard, good on you! But don't stop, there are plenty more!" Rudel yelled as he grabbed his rifle and fired over the silhouettes that, little by little, despite sustaining great losses, gradually managed to set foot on the beach.

Aboard the *USS Samuel Chase*, William Bishop suddenly stopped scribbling in his notebook. A man whose face seemed familiar to him was climbing up the stairs of a gangway, with a smile on his face.

Bishop wondered where he had already seen this stranger.

He was sure that it wasn't very long ago.

"Who's the guy with the cameras round his neck?" asked one of the GIs as he drank his coffee.

"That's Capa. Robert Capa[17]. He landed on Omaha with the first wave of assault. He's taken tons of photographs for Life magazine. He's a great guy!"

William suddenly remembered...

---

17. Of the hundred or so pictures take by Robert Capa on D-Day, only eleven survived following an error by a photographic laboratory assistant.

My friend James had just been hit. Swept out by a wave, I saw him drift away, shaking his arms before finally sinking to the seabed.

I turned round and aimed my rifle towards the small embankment from where the deadly gunfire had come when, suddenly, my eyes were drawn towards an incredible scene.

Something totally unimaginable. And yet...

Lying in the sand, hiding behind a Czech hedgehog, apparently totally indifferent to the hurricane of fire and steel that was crashing down all round him, a man was taking countless photographs of the battle that was ensuing before his very eyes.

He suddenly noticed me and, after a friendly wave, he continued to calmly take his pictures, pictures that would soon travel the world.

A few seconds later, incredibly cold-blooded, the photographer left his shelter, turned his back on the enemy bullets and aimed the lens of his Contax at a group of GIs that were cutting up a huge barbed wire fence.

Then, I lost him from sight...

On Omaha Beach, the landing was now turning into total carnage.

Along the beach, machines desperately tried to clear the way and to open a route for survivors across a maelstrom of wrecked vehicles and piled up bodies.

Overwhelmed nurses ran round in circles, with syringes and bags of plasma in their hands, doing *their best to tend to the most seriously wounded soldiers.*

A few yards from me, a captain was on his radio, his face covered in blood, imploring his superiors to send him reinforcements as quickly as possible.

When he saw me, hiding behind what remained of a small antitank wall, he screamed at me,

"Move, move my boy! Your only chance for survival is to move on, believe me! Soon, there'll only be dead men on this goddamned beach!"

He was probably right; all the more so since the second wave of assault was soon to be launched...

I was preparing to cautiously leave my shelter when a searing pain shot down my right leg.

It was so intense that I fainted almost on the spot...

Bloody Omaha

When I regained consciousness, I was lying on a blood-stained cover, laid on a part of the beach that was covered with pebbles and overlooked by a bunker, the occupants of which had been neutralised less than half an hour earlier by direct fire from a battleship.

All around me, swarms of doctors, surgeons, nurses and stretcher-bearers were bustling about.

They moved from one wounded soldier to another, rapidly sorting the different types of wounds, whilst evacuating, as quickly as they could, the bodies of those for whom nothing more could be done.

An officer stopped next to me and, as he pointed to two critically injured GIs who were going through agonies, he simply said, before moving on,

"We can save this one. It's too late for the other one. He's lost too much blood. Give his place to someone else."

Such was the fate of some on Omaha Beach on this morning of the 6th of June...

A little later, I hailed a male nurse and, to clear things up in my own mind, I asked him, as I pointed to my right leg,

"Is it serious?"

"It could've been worse! The doctor was wondering whether he shouldn't amputate. But he finally managed to save it. Don't worry! You'll be evacuated to England in the afternoon."

"No earlier?"

"No. We're not sure you can handle the journey right now, and we have priorities. As you can see for yourself, we barely know where to start here. I've got to leave you now; I'm needed for an urgent blood transfusion. Cheer up mate!"

As I leaned up on an elbow, the scene I discovered all around me was apocalyptic.

Almost everywhere across the shoreline, wrecked LCVPs[18] and LSTs[19] stood alongside the shells of tanks, jeeps, trucks and bulldozers along with hundreds of bodies still in their life jackets, tossed by the waves and incessantly beached on the sand by the tide.

The sky was reddened by fire, blackened by smoke, clouded by smoke bombs, as dozens of bombers escorted by hordes of fighter planes continued to drop tonnes of bombs on the last remaining resistance nests along this portion of the Atlantic Wall.

With distraught faces, surrounded by threatening GIs, the German soldiers, in their soiled or torn uniforms, were brutally grouped together near a bunker that had been destroyed by a large-calibre

18. Refer to glossary.
19. Refer to glossary.

shell and upon which the Star-Spangled Banner was now flying.

A short distance away, two SS soldiers in a sorry state were guarded by a Military Police sergeant before being interrogated.

Everywhere, the air was filled with a fetid and stubborn smell of blood and death, mixed with the odour of gunpowder and cordite.

A smell that, even years later, I will never be able to forget...

In the hope of escaping the depressing scene of this infernal beach, a few seconds later I set to contemplating the picture of Jenny and Sam. I was feeling terribly blue, and was struggling to hold back my tears.

In vain.

A GI whose chest was gradually disappearing under a huge bandage noticed the picture and said,

"Not bad that girl! I suppose she's your fiancée?"

I nodded and, almost mechanically, wiped away the tears that were now flowing over Jennifer's face.

It was really strange; on the photo, it was as if Sam and Jenny were also crying... crying over this immense waste for which the madness of men was, once more, alone to blame...

After...

William Bishop finally returned to England aboard the USS *Samuel Chase* hospital ship.

He was admitted to a clinic on the outskirts of London, where he stayed for several months. Thanks to his will and his courage, he eventually managed to walk again, almost normally, with the help of a stick.

Jennifer was quick to rush to the capital city to join him. She worked part-time as a babysitter and rented a small studio near to the Marble Arch, to be as close as possible to her fiancé.

Once or twice a week, weather permitting, William and Jenny took walks together in the park next to the clinic, or even romantic strolls along the banks of the Thames.

When they were together, just the two of them, they obviously made plans for the future; they imagined the simple and harmonious life that they would lead with their children as soon as William had totally recovered.

Then, strangely, one November afternoon in 1944, when they had planned to go to the cinema in Leicester Square, William waited for Jennifer, in vain.

He wasn't particularly worried; Jenny had intended to return to her home village for a few days to look after an old aunt who was poorly. Perhaps her aunt's condition had suddenly worsened and Jenny had been forced to bring forward her departure?

After a long week with no news from his fiancée, William sent a letter to Sparrowbridge; however, his letter, just like all the other letters he later wrote, received no reply.

William finally discovered a few months later that Jennifer, the one and only love of his life, had been buried beneath her house when it collapsed after being hit by a V2[20], Adolf Hitler's new weapon destined to terrorise Britain, in the autumn of 1944.

The young girl's body was never found.

In April 1945, exhausted and weighed down by sorrow, William Bishop decided to return to the United States where, for over thirty years, he occupied a position as sales representative for the vehicle manufacturer Ford.

He never married and lived a solitary life in a small house located on the banks of a mountain

---

20. Refer to glossary.

lake, with just his memories and several dogs adopted from a nearby refuge for company.

William's secret dream was to cross the Atlantic once more and to return to Normandy to, at least once more before he died, see Omaha Beach, the beach where he had landed under a deluge of fire from German guns and machine guns on the 6th of June 1944. The beach that was late to be referred to as Bloody Omaha.

He thought his dream would never come true, until one morning in February 2013. A Second World War Veterans' organisation was planning to organise a "Remembrance journey" to Normandy and to the 1944 battlefields.

William initially hesitated; would his old age – he was now 90 – enable him to make such a long journey and to cope with so much emotion? Then, just a few days before the closure of reservations, he finally decided to book a ticket, much to the joy of his rare friends who were all too aware of how important that French beach was to him...

Returning to Omaha

William Bishop was helped off the coach by the driver who had taken him, along with his group of veterans, to the American military cemetery in Colleville-sur-Mer.

Covering a surface area of around 70 hectares, the cemetery overlooks Omaha Beach, where over 2,500 young Americans lost their lives on D-Day...

"Take your time and be careful not to slide!" their guide advised them.

Bishop nodded before following a few veterans from the 82nd and the 101st Airborne Divisions along the main aisle of the immense necropolis.

He advanced aimlessly, moving from one line of graves to the next, deciphering from time to time a name, a date of birth, an affiliation to one or other regiment.

As he slowly progressed through the cemetery, William became increasingly immersed in emotion.

Emotion that was close to overwhelming him when he reached the Memorial.

After taking the time to admire the splendid monument in the form of a semicircular colonnade with a loggia at each extremity, William Bishop then headed for the Garden of the Missing, the walls of which are engraved with the names of some 1,600 soldiers who were never identified.

Quickly, William found the names of his two friends, James Mercury and Peter Johnson.

After a short prayer in their memory, he returned to the coach, in no great hurry.

His memories flocked back, whirling around, both in his head and in his heart.

"Mr Bishop, we're now going to visit Omaha Beach," announced the guide as soon as she saw him. "Since we're slightly ahead of schedule, you can stay there a little longer if you like. I hope that's good news for you."

*

A little later, as he paced up and down the promenade that runs alongside a now peaceful and deserted Omaha Beach – the very same beach where, sixty-nine years earlier, he had landed in the midst of Hell itself, William Bishop suddenly noticed another man, of roughly his own age, sitting on a stone bench and staring at a lone seagull as it flew across the English Channel.

William approached the stranger.

As he was about to shake his hand, he noticed the tears running down the old man's face.

"Hello. My name's Bishop. William Bishop. Were you with the *Big Red One* too?" he asked rather uncomfortably.

The man wiped his face with his coat sleeve, then he smiled, before replying in the gentlest of tones,

"No. I'm German. My name is Hans Kuerten. On the 6th of June, I was somewhere up there with my machine gun," he explained as he pointed to the ruins of a bunker overlooking the beach. For three hours, I killed dozens of guys like you before being taken prisoner. It was war, of course, but, how can I explain, the sight of those soldiers lying on the sand because of me haunts me day and night. Today, I am ill, incurably ill and I have very little time left to live. But I absolutely needed to come back here to try to exorcise that dark period of my existence. My granddaughter Elke," he added as he pointed to a blond woman aged around thirty who was sitting in a hired car, "she's kept me company so that I don't have to face all my ghosts from the past on my own."

William remained silent for a few seconds, before whispering in an emotive voice, "Hans.

Can I call you Hans? I was on that beach too, on the 6th of June 1944. Perhaps it was even a bullet from your machine gun that hit me?" he added as he showed Hans his leg. "After all these years, don't you think it's time to forget our shared guilt, our inner wounds and to forgive each other for the deaths caused by a war which we have both come to realise, a little late alas, was totally futile?"

"Of course. Of course, Kamerad William," Kuerten replied as he stood up to give him a fraternal hug.

Well aware that these two former enemies were experiencing an exceptional moment, William asked Hans,

"What are you going to do now?"

"I have no idea. I daresay I'll pay a visit to the graves of my compatriots, who are buried in the La Cambe[21] cemetery. Apparently, it's not far from here."

William hesitated a few seconds, then, suddenly, he took the former Panzergrenadier by the hand and he asked him with much kindness as he looked deep into his eyes,

"Hans, would you mind if I came with you?"

"I..."

"Please, don't say no, please... I beg you, Kamerad..."

---

21. One of the largest German cemeteries in Normandy. Located between Bayeux and Isigny, it is home to 21,160 graves.

Contents

HISTORICAL REFERENCES

AND

DOCUMENTS

Glossary

Belgian gate: antitank obstacle designed to reinforce the defensive line between Belgium and Germany. An example can still be seen at the *Omaha Beach* Museum in Saint-Laurent-sur-Mer.

Czech hedgehog: an antitank obstacle composed of 180 cm steel beams or corner irons. This device was initially deployed on the border between Germany and Czechoslovakia.

Jeep: this is one of the Second World War's most symbolic vehicles. Simple, sturdy, capable of transporting four passengers and 250 kilos of equipment, Jeeps were built in large numbers by Bantam, Willys and Ford.

Kieffer Commando: a group of 177 French soldiers who landed on the beach in Ouistreham on the 6th of June 1944. They were commanded by captain Philippe Kieffer.

GI: This abbreviation does not stand for General Infantry, but stems from the term Galvanized Iron, which was used on many products provided to troops, in particular on their ration boxes. By extension, GI applies to all government supplies, hence the reference to Government Issue.

LCVP (Landing Craft Vehicle Personnel): the smallest landing barge - 11 metres long (36 feet) - capable of carrying 30 soldiers and their kit.

LST (Landing Ship Tank): landing ship capable of transporting 2,000 tonnes of equipment. Of a length of 98 metres (321 feet), the LST was equipped with a 40mm gun and with sixty 20mm guns. The manner in which its double bow door opened enabled it to land machines, vehicles and equipment directly on the beach.

Rommel's Asparagus: among the defensive systems installed on the beaches along the coast of the English Channel and the North Sea, Rommel's asparagus are particularly worthy of note. They were in the form of wooden spikes, sometimes topped with a mine, intended to break open the landing barges as they passed over them.

The Atlantic Wall: series of fortifications set up by the Germans to prevent and contain any risk of invasion from the sea. During his first inspections, Rommel detected a number of failings in the Atlantic Wall. He reconsidered the main obstacles and the defensive devices that protected the beaches.

The Battle of Britain: after having invaded Belgium and France, Hitler dreamed of landing in England. He launched his air force, the *Luftwaffe*, against the country's main infrastructures, ports, airports and industrial centres. From July to September 1940, the *Royal Air Force* determinedly defied its adversary, who finally surrendered.

V2: abbreviation of the German word *Vergeltungwaffe* (retaliation weapon), the V2, which replaced the V1, was a missile with a range of 320 kilometres (200 miles) and a speed close to 5,500 km/h (3,400 mph). Launched in England as from September 1944, it was responsible for the death of many civilians.

A TOUS LES FRANÇAIS

La France a perdu une bataille!
Mais la France n'a pas perdu la guerre!

Des gouvernants de rencontre ont pu capituler, cédant à la panique, oubliant l'honneur, livrant le pays à la servitude. Cependant, rien n'est perdu!

Rien n'est perdu, parce que cette guerre est une guerre mondiale. Dans l'univers libre, des forces immenses n'ont pas encore donné. Un jour, ces forces écraseront l'ennemi. Il faut que la France, ce jour-la, soit présente à la victoire. Alors, elle retrouvera sa liberté et sa grandeur. Tel est mon but, mon seul but!

Voilà pourquoi je convie tous les Francais, où qu'ils se trouvent, à s'unir à moi dans l'action, dans le sacrifice et dans l'espérance.

Notre patrie est en péril de mort.
Luttons tous pour la sauver!

VIVE LA FRANCE !

JUIN, 1940

GÉNÉRAL DE GAULLE

Poster of De Gaulle's appeal of the 18th of June.

Chronological references

January 1933: Adolf Hitler becomes Chancellor of Germany.

September 1939: the Second World War begins.

May 1940: France is invaded.

18th June 1940: General de Gaulle's appeal.

July to September 1940: Battle of Britain.

7th December 1941: The United States enter the war following the Japanese attack on Pearl Harbor.

August 1943: The First Quebec Conference agrees on the principle of an Allied landing operation in Normandy.

6th June 1944: Allied Landings in Normandy.

15th August 1944: Allied Landings in Provence.

25th August 1944: Paris is liberated.

December 1944: Battle of the Bulge.

April 1945: Death of Adolf Hitler in the ruins of Berlin.

8th May 1945: Germany surrenders.

September 1945: Japan signs its surrender aboard the battleship *Missouri*. The Second World War finally comes to an end.

"Rommel's asparagus".

Historic figures

Dwight Eisenhower (1890-1969)

Nicknamed "Ike", Dwight Eisenhower was the commander of the Allied forces in North Africa, then in Italy. After the Tehran Conference, he was appointed supreme commander of the Allied armies in Europe and took over one of the greatest operations in military history: the Normandy landings. After the war, he became a politician, accomplishing a brilliant career that earned him the Presidency of the United States from 1952 to 1960.

Sir Bernard Montgomery (1887-1976)

It was in the desert sand that Montgomery established his renown thanks to his victory at El Alamein. In January 1944, he was appointed as Eisenhower's deputy, devoting his time and energy to the preparations for the D-Day Landings. He commanded the British troops that were kept at a virtual standstill on the outskirts of Caen for several long weeks.

Sir Winston Churchill (1874-1965)

The United Kingdom's Prime Minister during the Second World War, he stated to his fellow citizens that all he had to offer them was "blood, toil, tears and sweat." He supported General de Gaulle, against the Americans. His "Memoirs of the Second World War" earned him the Nobel Prize for Literature.

Franklin Delano Roosevelt (1882-1945)

He was elected President of the United States for the first time in 1933, to be re-elected in 1936 and 1940. He took the decision to send his nation to war after the Japanese attack on the Pearl Harbor base in December 1941. He maintained regular contact with Winston

Churchill and Joseph Stalin in order to lead the Allies into final victory that he was not to see, for he died after suffering a long period of illness, just a few weeks before the German surrender.

Charles de Gaulle (1890-1970)

General de Gaulle went down in History following his appeal of the 18th of June. Founder of the French Free Forces, during the war, he personified the image of an unyielding France whose desire was to continue to fight. Excluded from the final D-Day Landing preparations, he hastily travelled to Normandy and made an important speech in  Bayeux on the 14th of June 1944 in order to thwart the American plans to place France under their control.

Field Marshal Erwin Rommel (1891-1944)

After having fought in the First World War, he was appointed general in 1939, brilliantly distinguishing himself with his armoured unit in the French campaign. His presence in Libya, in charge of the Afrika Korps, earned him the

epithet of the "Desert Fox". Late 1943, he was appointed to supervise the coastal defences that stretched from the Spanish border to the North Sea. He was involved in the plot to assassinate Hitler on the 20th of July 1944 and was coerced into suicide.

Rommel and a group of German officers inspecting the coastal defenses.

Map of the Battle of Normandy

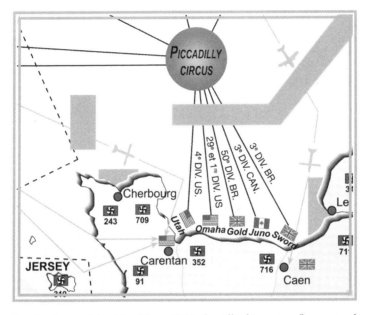

On the dawn of the 6th of June 1944, the Allied invasion fleet arrived before the Normandy coast.

To the west, the American forces that comprised Force U landed at La Madeleine in the *Utah Beach* sector.

Force O attacked the zone codenamed *Omaha Beach*, stretching from Vierville to Sainte-Honorine-des-Pertes.

Then followed the British sector with *Gold Beach*, between Graye-sur-Mer and Arromanches, *Juno Beach* between Graye-sur-Mer and Luc-sur-Mer and *Sword Beach* between the mouth of the River Orne in Ouistreham and Lion-sur-Mer.

It was on *Sword Beach* that the 177 French soldiers from the Kieffer commando braved the enemy.

Geographical map of the *Omaha Beach* sector

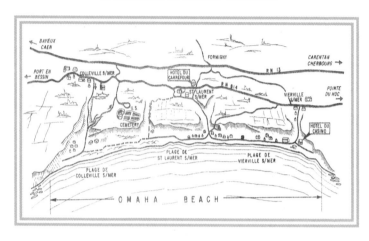

Landing barges approaching *Omaha Beach*.

Major museums associated with the Battle of Normandy

- Arromanches – D-Day Museum and 360°circular cinema
- Bayeux – Battle of Normandy Memorial Museum
- Caen – Memorial centre for history and peace
- Cherbourg – Liberation Museum
- Colleville-sur-Mer – *Overlord Museum*
- Courseulles-sur-Mer – *Juno Beach* Centre
- Douvres-la-Délivrande – Radar Museum
- Grandcamp Maisy – Rangers Museum
- Merville Franceville – Battle of Merville Museum
- Montormel – Battle of Normandy Museum
- Ouistreham-Riva Bella – N°4 Commando Museum, Atlantic Wall Museum and "Grand Bunker"
- Quinéville – Memorial of newfound freedom
- Ranville – Pegasus Memorial
- Saint-Côme-du-Mont – D-Day Paratroopers Historic Centre
- Saint-Laurent-sur-Mer – *Omaha Beach* Memorial Museum
- Sainte-Marie-du-Mont – *Utah Beach* Landing Museum
- Sainte-Mère-Église – Airborne Museum
- Ver-sur-Mer – America-*Gold Beach* Museum
- Vierville – D-Day *Omaha* Museum

Brief bibliography

CARRELL Paul, *Ils arrivent !*, Robert Laffont, 1962.

FLORENTIN Eddy, *Le Guide des plages du débarquement et de la bataille de Normandie*, Perrin, 2003.

FLORENTIN Eddy, *Stalingrad en Normandie*, Presses de la Cité, 1964.

HOWARTH David, *6 juin à l'aube*, Presses de la Cité, 1959 (also available in English).

KIEFFER Philippe, *Béret vert*, France-Empire, 1952.

MORDAL Jacques, *La bataille de France*, Arthaud, 1972.

PERRAULT Gilles, *Le Grand Jour*, J.-C. Lattès, 1974.

PERRAULT Gilles, *Le secret du Jour J*, Fayard, 1994.

QUELLIEN Jean, *Les Américains en Normandie*, Orep, 2012 (also available in English).

QUELLIEN Jean, *Normandie 44*, Orep, 2011 (also available in English).

RYAN Cornélius, *Le Jour le plus long*, Robert Laffont, 1959 (also available in English).

Filmography on the Normandy Landings

ESWAY Alexander, *They are not Angels*, 1947.

FULLER Samuel, *The Big Red One*, 1980.

MCLAGLEN Andrew Victor, *The Breakthrough*, 1978.

PARRISH Robert, *Up from the beach*, 1965.

SPIELBERG Steven, *Saving Private Ryan*, 1998.

ZANUCK Darryl F., *The Longest Day*, 1962.

A few other works by Patrick Bousquet-Schneeweis

Bleu chien soleil des tranchées, Serpenoise.

Chance, les ailes de la liberté, Serpenoise.

Félin pour l'autre !, followed by *Même les souris ont du chagrin !*, co-written with his cat Scot, Les 3 Orangers.

Héros du Jour J, Orep (also available in English).

La Balle rouge (preface by Raymond Aubrac), Orep (also available in English).

La Banquise a croqué le Chat noir, Serpenoise (Prix littéraire des Vosges Young Reader's Prize 2006).

Les neiges de l'enfer, Serpenoise.

Lucie et Raymond Aubrac, Editions Oskar.

Shootings (preface by Gilles Perrault), Les 3 Orangers ("Raconte-moi l'Histoire" Youth Prize, 2012).

Un tank nommé Éternité, Serpenoise.

A few other works by Michel Giard

Chansons de marins, Orep.

Chansons normandes, du Cotentin à la plaine de Caen, Orep.

La carriole, Editions Isoète.

La grande histoire du sauvetage en mer, Le Télégramme.

Le carnet de cuisine du Cotentin, Le Télégramme.

Le Dictionnaire du Cotentin, Le Télégramme

Les grandes catastrophes maritimes du XXe siècle, Editions P. Galodé.

Les mousses, de Colbert à nos jours, Le Télégramme.

Phares et feux de Normandie, Orep.

Prendre pied, tenir ou mourir, Editions P. Galodé.

OREP

EDITIONS

Zone tertiaire de Nonant – 14400 BAYEUX
Tel: 02 31 51 81 31 – **Fax:** 02 31 51 81 32
info@orepeditions.com – www.orepeditions.com

Editor: Grégory PIQUE
Conception design: Éditions OREP
Graphics and layout: Sophie YOUF
Editorial coordination: Aurélien BRAULT
English translation: Heather COSTIL

From the same collection

The BLOODY MAPLES
Juno Beach, 6th June 1944

by Patrick Bousquet-Schneeweis and Michel Giard

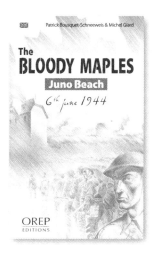

– *Marcel Ouimet from Radio Canada here. I am with men from the Régiment de La Chaudière before a small seaside resort called Bernières-sur-Mer.*
Shellfire from the German artillery batteries is intensifying all around us! The order is finally given to attack!
I can imagine the emotion felt by our troops during these historic moments, for many of them have French blood in them.

From Montreal to *Juno Beach*, the incredible Canadian odyssey which, on the 6th of June 1944, contributed towards our newfound freedom...

Photographic credits

Cover illustrations: Jean-François Miniac
p. 64, 67, 68, 69, 70, 72: Michel Giard collection
p. 71: Map by CRHQ
p. 72: US National Archives

ISBN: 978-2-8151-0156-1

© Editions OREP 2013